Houghton Mifflin California Math

Practice

Student Book

Visit **Education Place®**
www.eduplace.com/kids

GRADE

K

 HOUGHTON MIFFLIN   BOSTON

Printed in the U.S.A.

ISBN 10: 0-547-17350-4
ISBN 13: 978-0-547-17350-4

12 0982 15 14 13 12
4500362182

Name _____

Hands On: Top, Middle, Bottom

CA Standard
MG 2.2

Directions: Color the item in the middle green, the item on top red, and the item on the bottom yellow.

Before, After, Between

CA Standard
MG 2.2

Directions: **1** Circle the rabbit that is before the animal in a cap. **2** Circle the animal that is after the one in a cap. **3.** Circle the animal that is before the one in a cap. **4** Circle the animal that is between the ones in caps.

Use with text pp. 7–8

Inside, Outside

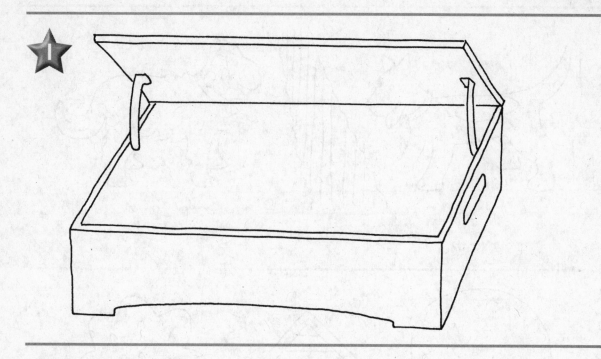

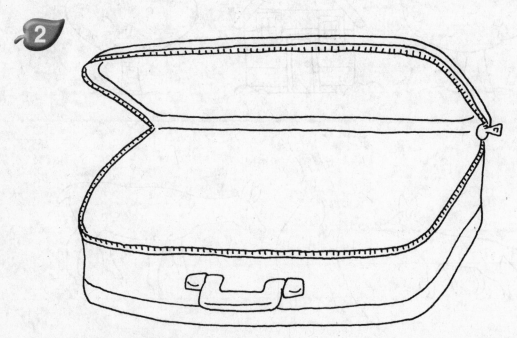

Directions: 1 Draw something blue inside the toy box. Draw something orange outside the toy box.
2 Draw something green inside the suitcase. Draw something red outside the suitcase.

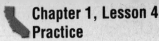
Hands On: Left and Right

CA Standard
MG 2.2

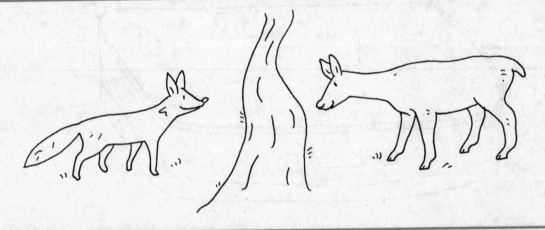

Directions: 1 Color the dog on the left blue and the one on the right red. **2** Color the tree on the left green and the one on the right yellow. **3** Color the animal on the left orange and the one on the right brown.

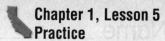
Problem Solving: Act It Out

⭐ 1

Directions: Circle the child who is inside. Cross out the child who is outside. Cross out the animal that is to the right of the girl. Cross out the bike that is under the tree. Circle the book that is below the desk.

Hands On: Same and Different

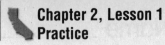

CA Standard
KEY AF 1.1

Directions: Circle the flowers that are alike. Cross out the one that is different.

Name _____

Hands On: Sort by Color

CA Standard
KEY AF 1.1

Directions: Circle the pictures that are the same color.

Name _____

Hands On: Sort by Size

CA Standard
KEY AF 1.1

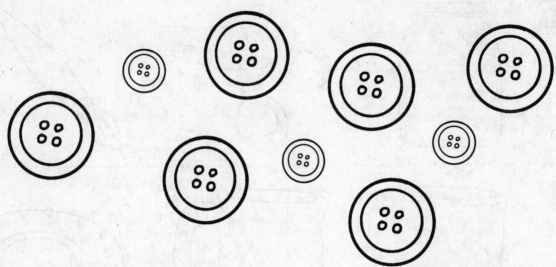

Directions: **1** Color the big buttons red. **2** Color the small stamps blue.

Use with text pp. 21–22

Hands On: Sort by Shape

CA Standard
KEY AF 1.1, MG 2.2

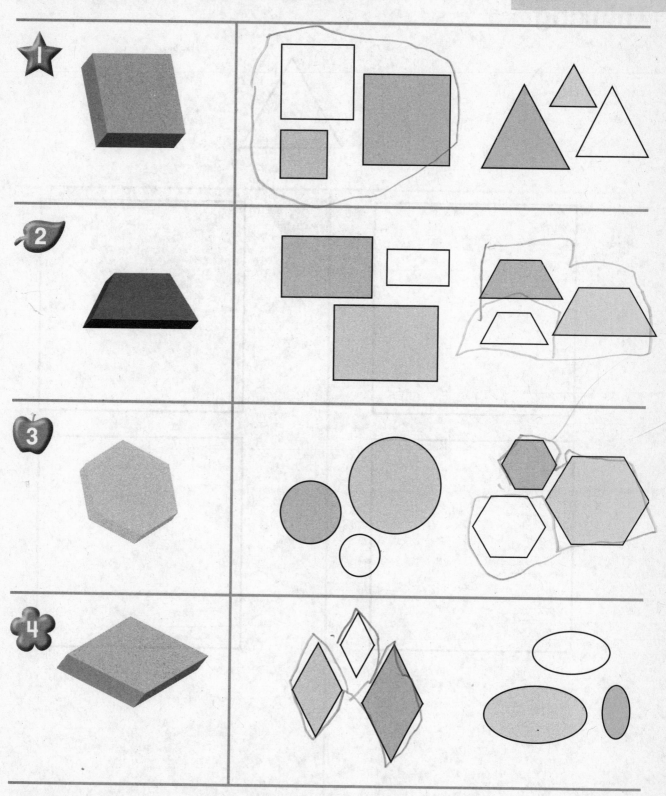

Directions: Circle the group where the shape belongs.

Name _____

Problem Solving: Logical Thinking

CA Standard
KEY AF 1.1, MG 2.2

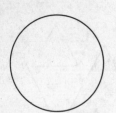 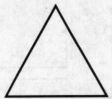

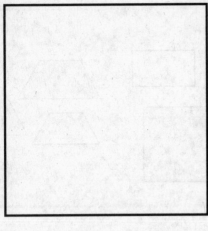

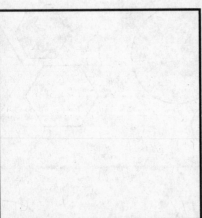

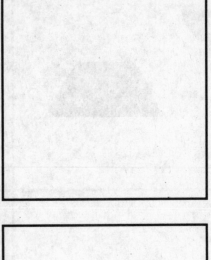

Directions: Find two different ways to sort the blocks. Draw and color the blocks. Explain your thinking.

Hands On: Some, All, and None

CA Standard
KEY AF 1.1

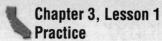

Directions: **1** Color all cars yellow. **2** Color some cars red. **3** Color some cars yellow. **4** Color the cars. Make none of them yellow.

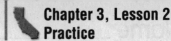

Hands On: Graph With Real Objects

CA Standard
SDAP 1.1

How Many of Each?

Directions: Cut out each box and paste the picture in the correct column.

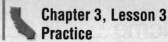
Hands On: Sort and Graph Coins

CA Standard
SDAP 1.1

Directions: Count each kind of coin at the top of the page. Color the boxes to show how many.

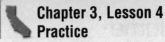

Picture Graphs

Fun at the Farm

Directions: Read the graph. Write the number that shows how many.

Problem Solving: Make a Graph

CA Standard
SDAP 1.1, MR 1.2

Ways to Get to School

Directions: Look at the picture. Color the graph to show how each child in the picture gets to school.

Use with text pp. 35–36

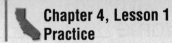

Hands On: Sort Plane Shapes

CA Standard
KEY AF 1.1

Directions: **1** Color the circles. **2** Color the triangles. **3** Color the rectangles. **4** Color the squares.

Name _____

Circle or Square

CA Standard
MG 2.1, NS 1.2

Directions: 1 Color the circles yellow. Write the number. 2 Color the squares green. Write the number.

Practice Book
17
Use with text pp. 51–52

Name _____

Rectangle or Triangle

CA Standard
MG 2.1, NS 1.2

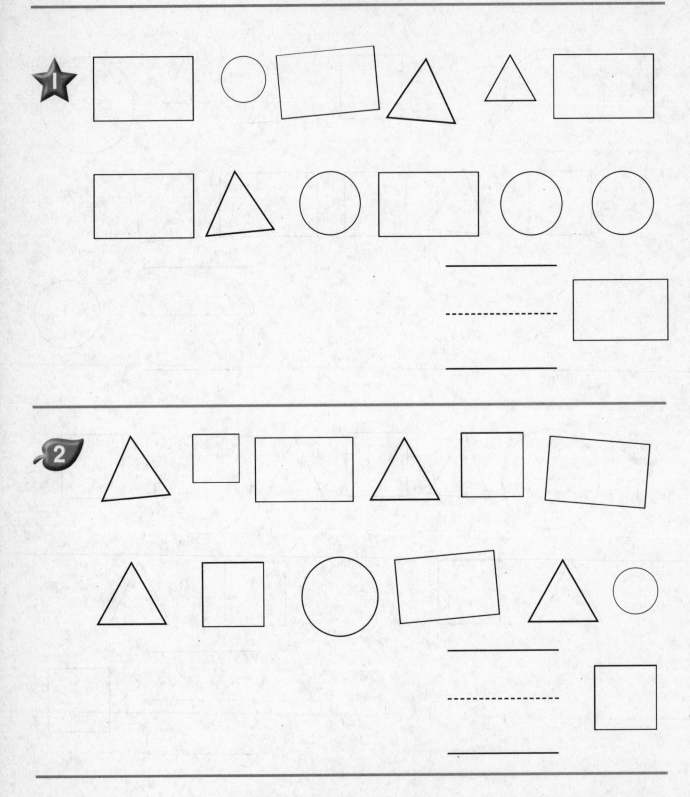

Directions: 1 Color the rectangles yellow. Write the number. **2** Color the triangles blue. Write the number.

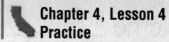

Name _____

Problem Solving: Draw a Picture

CA Standard
MG 2.1

Directions: Draw a picture with shapes. Color each kind of shape a different color.

Name _____

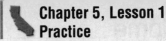
Hands On: Rhythmic Patterns

CA Standard
KEY SDAP 1.2

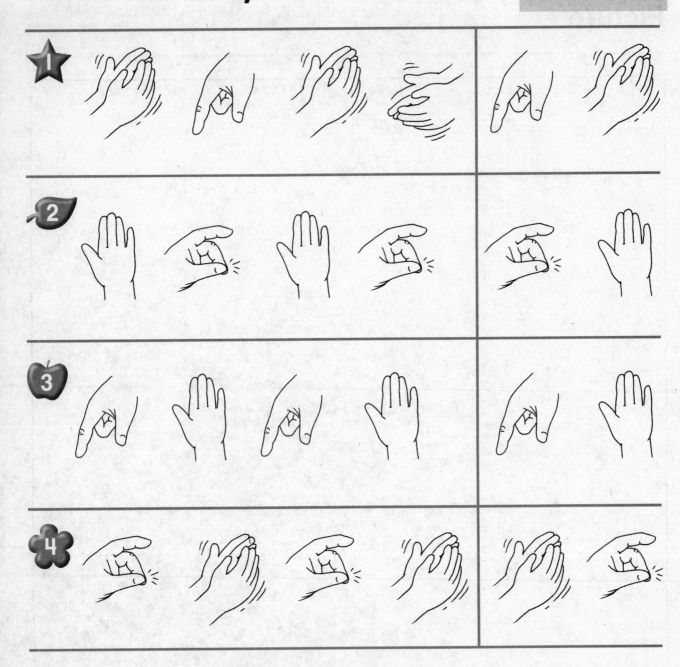

Directions: Look at the pattern. Circle the picture that shows what action is likely
to come next in the pattern.

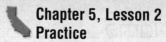
Hands On: Color Patterns

**CA Standard
KEY SDAP 1.2**

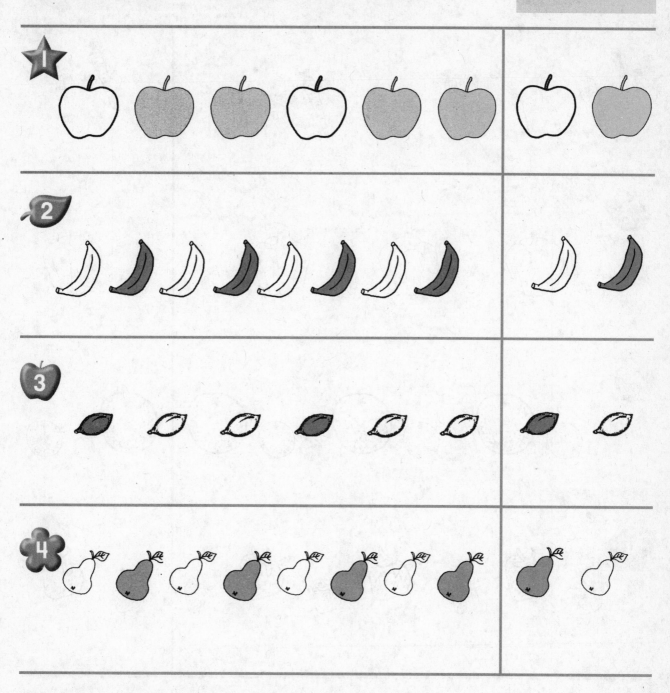

Directions: Find a pattern. Circle the item that is likely to come next in the pattern.

Use with text pp. 61–62

Name _____

Size Patterns

CA Standard
KEY SDAP 1.2

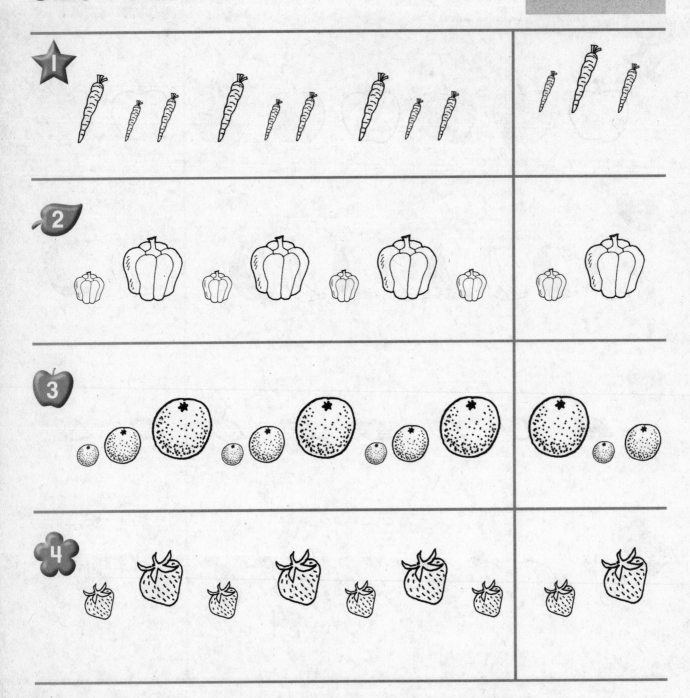

Directions: Find a pattern. Circle the item that is likely to come next in the pattern.

Name _____

Hands On: Patterns With Plane Shapes

CA Standard
KEY SDAP 1.2, MG 2.2

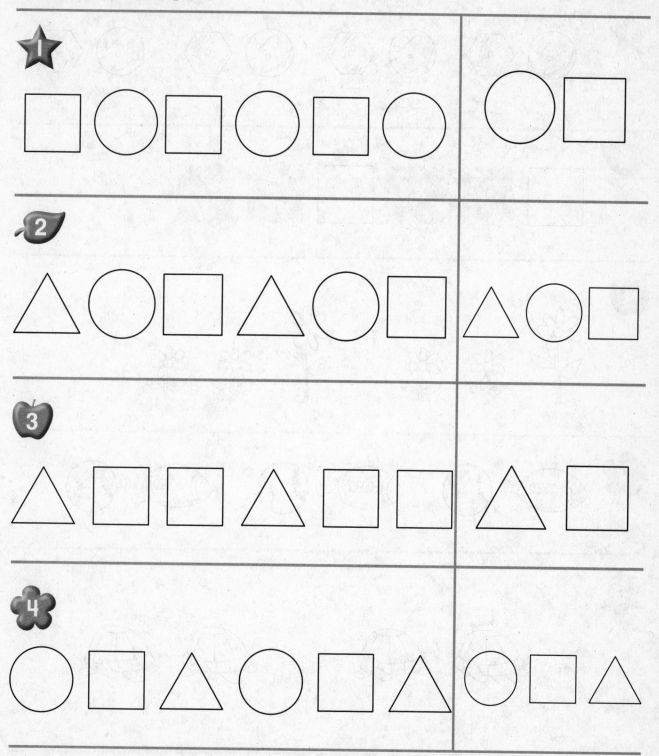

Directions: Find a pattern. Circle the shape that will likely come next in the pattern.

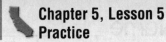
Problem Solving: Find a Pattern

CA Standards
KEY SDAP 1.2, MR 2.0

Directions: Look at the pattern. Circle the part of the pattern that repeats. Name the type of pattern.

Name _____

Hands On: Patterns and Positions

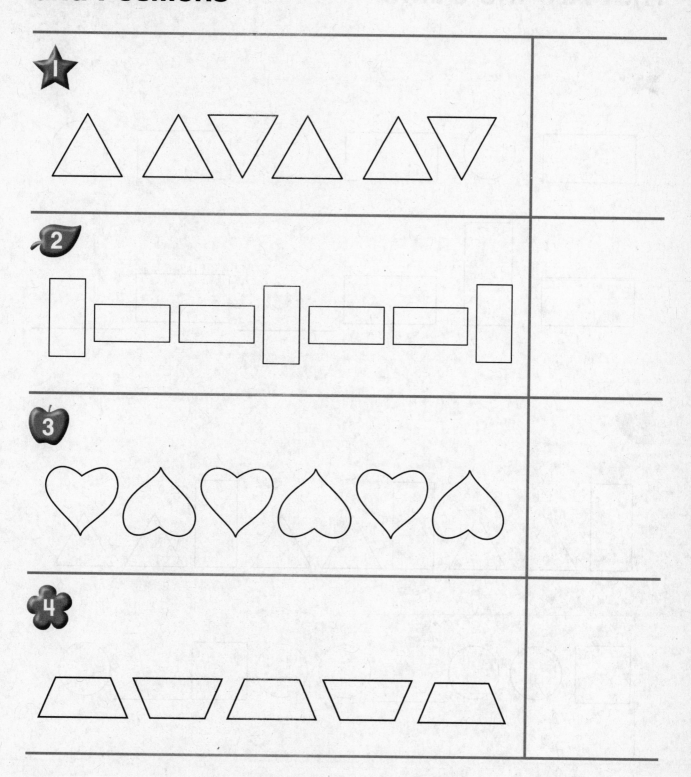

Directions: Find a pattern. Draw the shape that is likely to come next in the pattern.

25

Hands On: Patterns That Are the Same

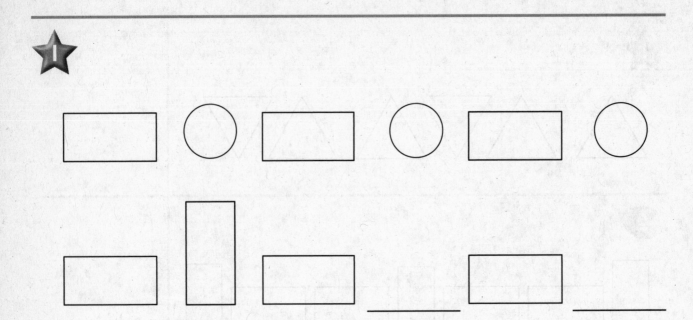

Directions: 1-2 Find a pattern. Draw the missing shapes in the pattern. Keep the same pattern from the first row.

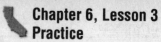
Hands On: Make Patterns

CA Standard
KEY SDAP 1.2

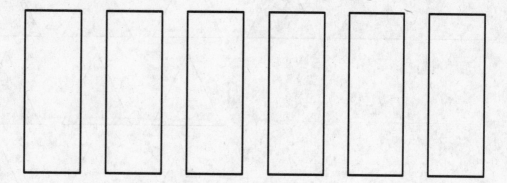

Directions: 1 Think of a color pattern. Color the rectangles to show your pattern.
2 Use rectangles in different positions to show a pattern.

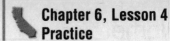

Problem Solving: Find a Pattern

CA Standard
KEY SDAP 1.2

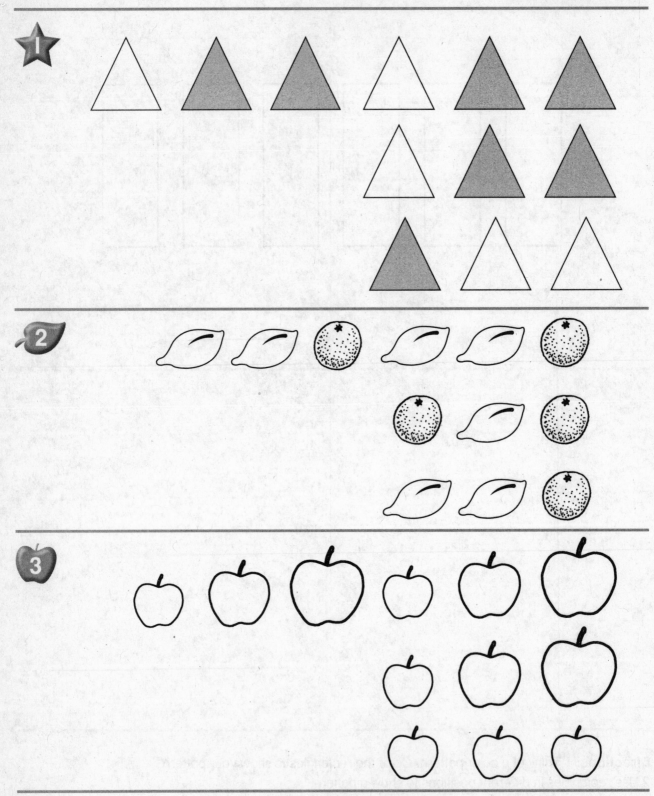

Directions: Find a pattern. Circle the group that is likely to come next.

Name _____

Hands On: One-to-One Correspondence

CA Standard
KEY NS 1.0

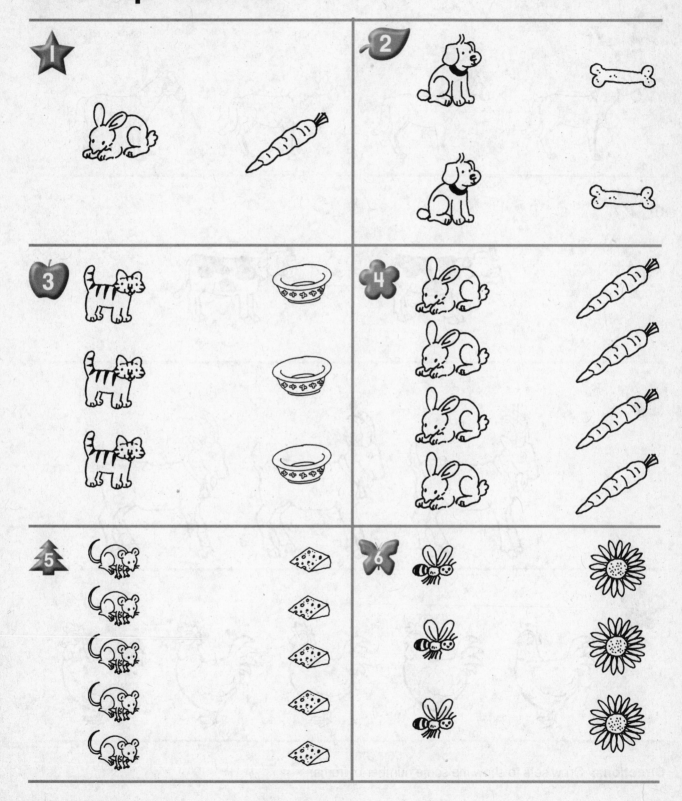

Directions: Draw lines to match the items one to one.

Use with text pp. 92B–92C

Hands On: Equal Sets

CA Standard
NS 1.1

Directions: Draw sets to show the same number of items.

Name _____

Hands On: More

CA Standard
NS 1.1

Directions: Count the items in each set. Color the set that has more.

Use with text pp. 95–96

Name _____

Hands On: Less

CA Standard
NS 1.1

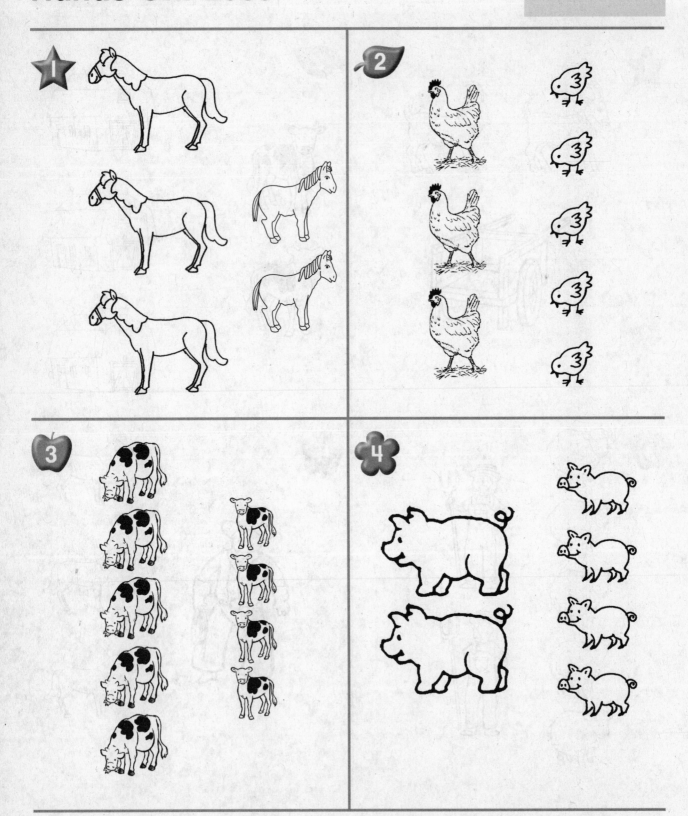

Directions: Match the items one to one. Circle the set that has fewer.

Name _____

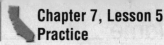
Problem Solving: Draw a Picture

CA Standard
NS 1.1

Directions: **1** Draw a set with more. **2** Draw a set with less. **3** Draw a set with the same number.

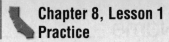

Hands On: Count and Read Numbers 1–3

CA Standard
NS 1.2

 1

1
2
3

2

1
2
3

3

1
2
3

4

1
2
3

Directions: Count the animals. Circle the number.

Name _____

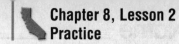
Hands On: One and Two

Directions: Count the items and write the number.

Name _____

Hands On: Three

Directions: Count each set and write the number. Then color each set of 3.

Name _____

Numbers 1-3

CA Standard
NS 1.2

Directions: Count and write the number of animals in each set.

Name _____

Problem Solving: Use a Graph

Directions: 1 Count the number of each animal shown in the graph and write the number.
2–3 Circle the animal with more in the graph.

Name _____

Hands On: Four

CA Standard
KEY NS 1.0

Directions: Count each set and write the number. Then circle each set of four.

Hands On: Five

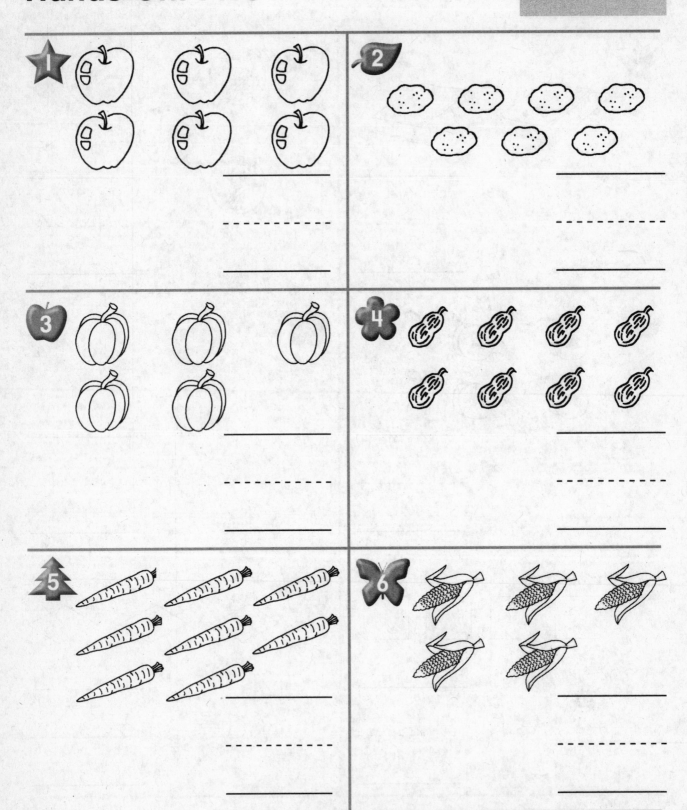

Directions: Color five items in each set. Then write the number 5.

Name _____

Hands On: Zero

Directions: Write how many of the item are in the picture.

Name _____

Numbers 0–5

CA Standard
NS 1.2

_____

- - - - - - - - - - - - - -

_____

_____

- - - - - - - - - - - - - -

_____

_____

- - - - - - - - - - - - - -

_____

_____

- - - - - - - - - - - - - -

_____

_____

- - - - - - - - - - - - - -

_____

_____

- - - - - - - - - - - - - -

_____

_____

- - - - - - - - - - - - - -

_____

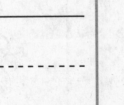 

_____

- - - - - - - - - - - - - -

_____

Directions: Write the number that shows how many animals.

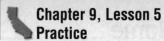
Problem Solving: Use a Picture

CA Standard
NS 1.2

Directions: Count the number of each animal in the picture. Write the number below the animal.

Hands On: Count and Read Numbers 1–7

CA Standard
NS 1.2

1   **2**   3

5   6   **7**

3   4   **5**

2   **3**   4

Directions: Count the animals. Circle the number.

Name _____

Hands On: Six

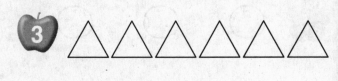

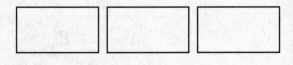

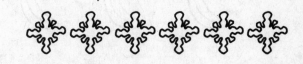

Directions: Circle the sets of 6. Write the number.

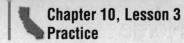
Hands On: Seven

CA Standard
KEY NS 1.0

_____

– – – – – – –

_____

_____

– – – – – – –

_____

Directions: Count the items. Draw more to make a set of 7. Write the number.

Name _____

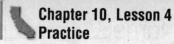
Show Parts 3–7

CA Standard
KEY NS 1.0

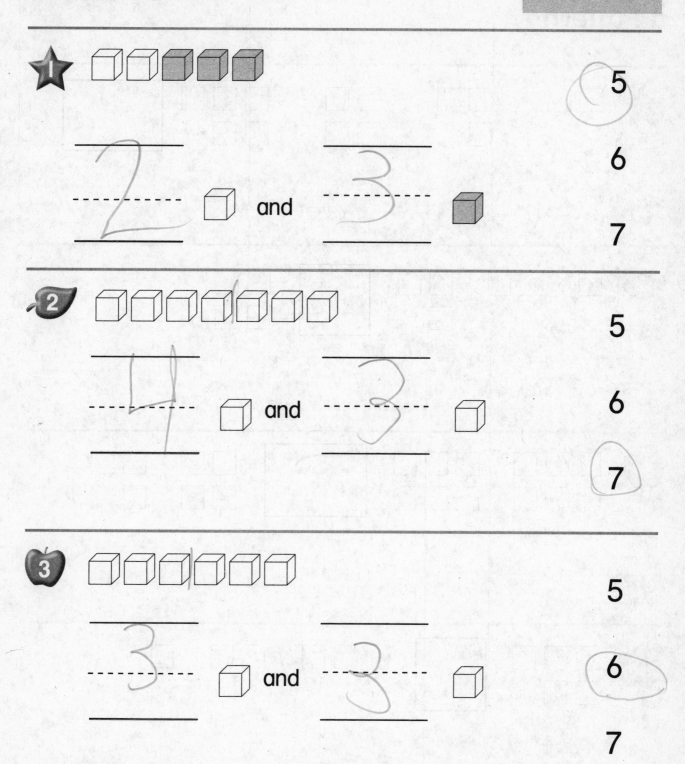

⭐ 1

___2___ 🧊 and ___3___ 🧊

(5) 6 7

🍃 2

___4___ 🧊 and ___3___ 🧊

5 6 (7)

🍎 3

___3___ 🧊 and ___3___ 🧊

5 (6) 7

Directions: 1 Count the cubes. Name and circle the number. **2–3** Color
some cubes one color and the rest another color. Name and write the number
of each color.

Use with text pp. 141–142

Name _____

Problem Solving: Look for a Pattern

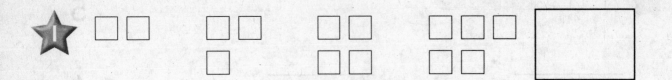

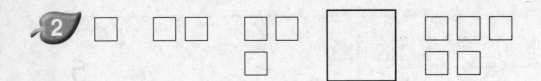

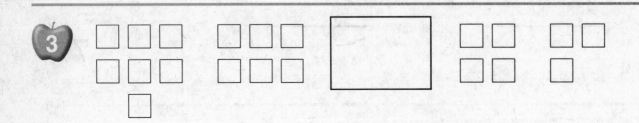

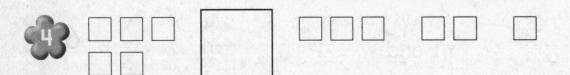

Directions: Find the number pattern. Draw the number of squares that is likely to come next in the empty box.

Name _____

Hands On: Eight

CA Standard
KEY NS 1.0

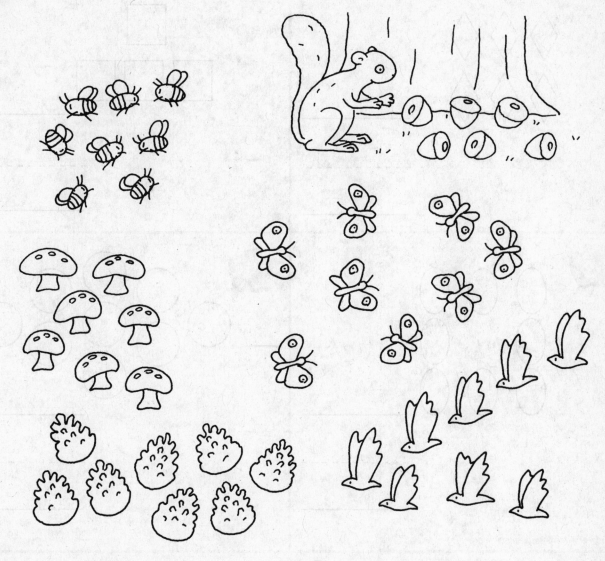

 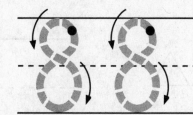

Directions: 1 Circle the groups of 8. **2** Write the number four more times.

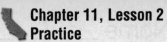

Hands On: Nine

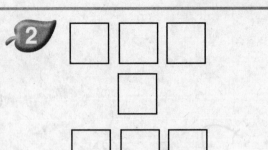

_____

- - - - - - - - -

_____

_____

- - - - - - - - -

_____

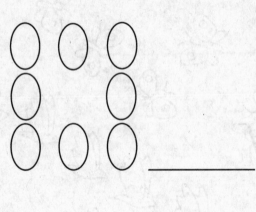

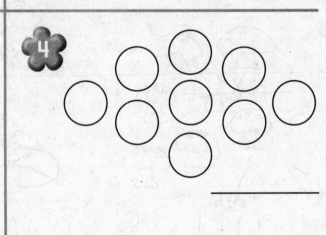

_____

- - - - - - - - -

_____

_____

- - - - - - - - -

_____

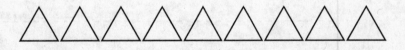

_____

- - - - - - - - -

_____

Directions: Count the shapes. Write the number.

Name _____

Hands On: Ten

CA Standard
NS 1.2

 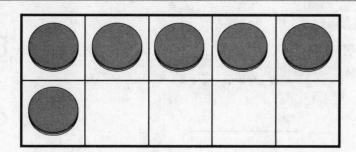

_____

_____

 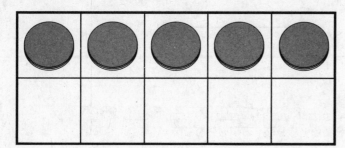

_____

_____

 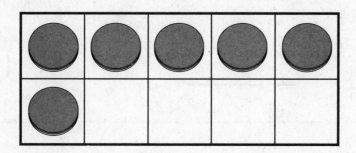

_____

_____

 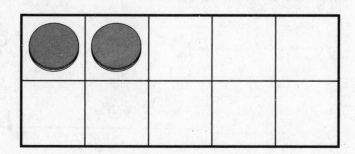

_____

_____

Directions: Draw counters in the ten-frame to make 10. Write the number.

Practice Book

51

Use with text pp. 153–154

Name _____

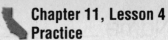
Hands On: Show Parts 8–10

CA Standard
NS 1.2

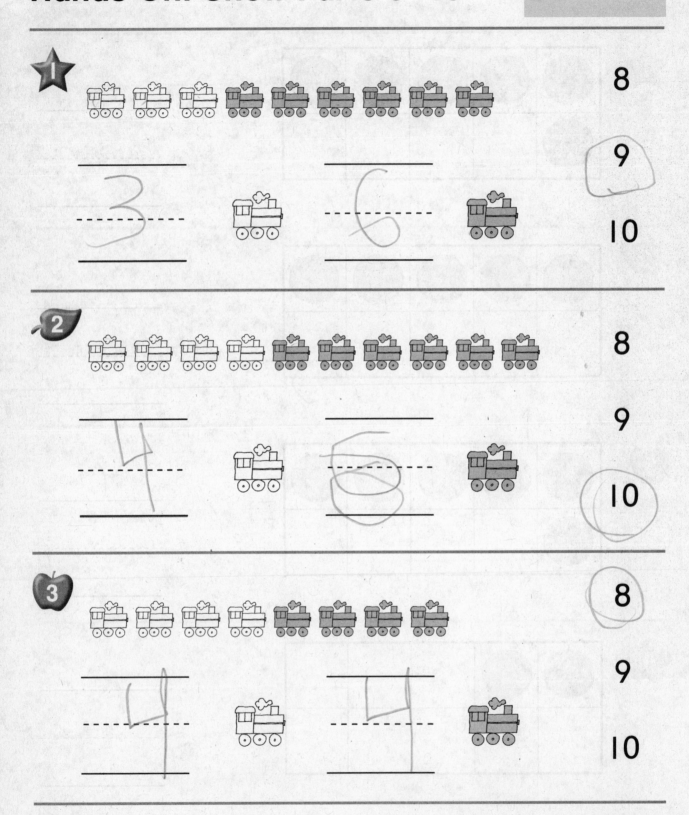

Directions: Count the number of trains. Circle the number. Count the trains of each color. Write the numbers.

Use with text pp. 154A–154D

Name _____

Problem Solving: Use a Picture

CA Standard
NS 1.2

_____

- - - - - - - - - -

_____

_____

- - - - - - - - - -

_____

_____

- - - - - - - - - -

_____

_____

- - - - - - - - - -

_____

Directions: Count the animals shown. Write the number. Color the sets that show ten.

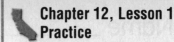

Hands On: Sort by Number

CA Standard
NS 1.2

Directions: Count each set of animals. Use a red crayon to circle sets of seven. Use a blue crayon to circle sets of ten.

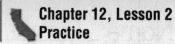
Order Numbers to 10

CA Standard
NS 1.2

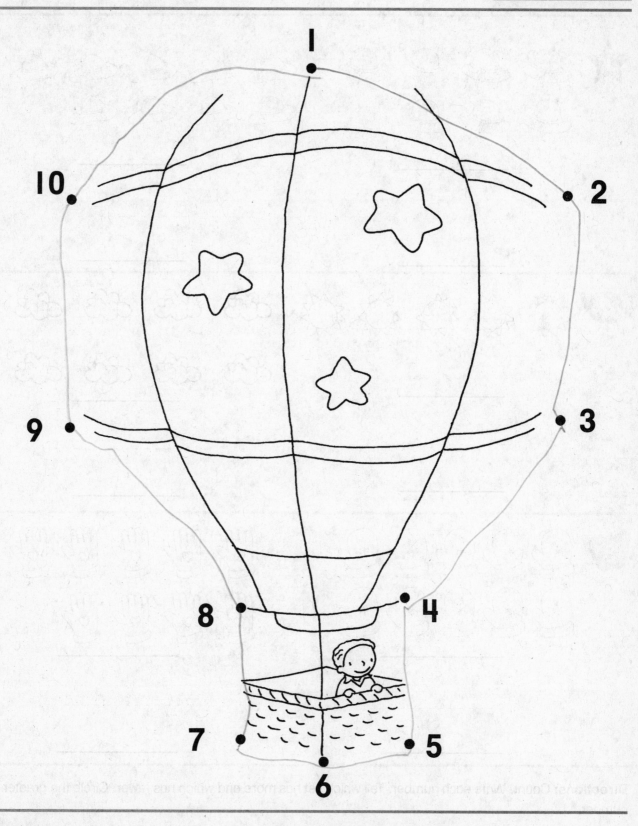

Directions: Connect the dots in numerical order to make a picture. Color the picture.

More and Less

_____
- - - - - - - - - - - -
_____

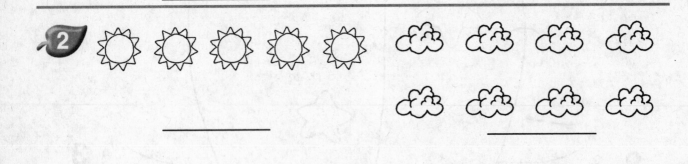

_____
- - - - - - - - - - - -
_____

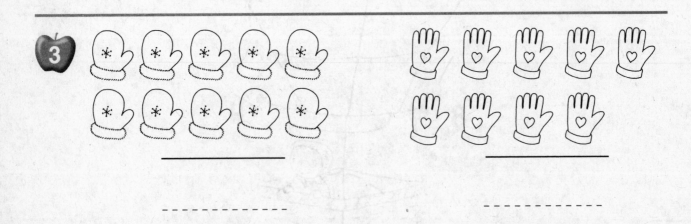

_____
- - - - - - - - - - - -

Directions: Count. Write each number. Tell which set has more and which has fewer. Circle the greater number.

Hands On: Ordinal Numbers

CA Standard
NS 1.2

Directions: Draw a blue circle around the second child getting into the bus. Draw a green circle around the tenth child. Draw a red circle around the seventh child.

Name _____

Problem Solving: Use a Graph

Animals at the Pet Fair

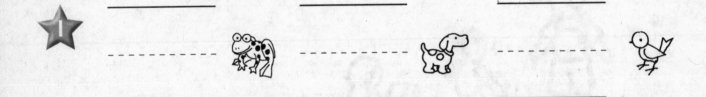

Directions: 1 Count and write the number of each kind of animal. **2–3** Circle the picture of the animal from the set that has more.

Hands On: Model Addition

CA Standard
KEY NS 2.1

 1
 4

2
  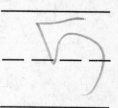 5

3
  9

 4
  7

Directions: Tell a story about the picture. Use counters to model the story. Count. Write how many in all.

Name _____

Hands On: Add with Cubes

CA Standard
KEY NS 2.1

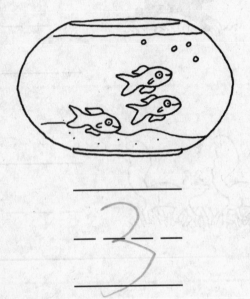

_____ 3 _____   _____ 2 _____

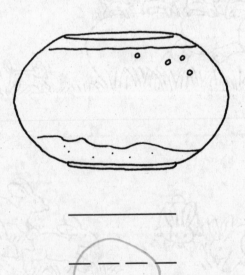

_____ 6 _____

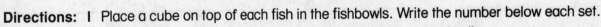

Directions: 1 Place a cube on top of each fish in the fishbowls. Write the number below each set.
2 Move all the cubes to the big fishbowl and trace them. Write how many in all.

Name _____

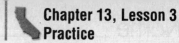
Hands On: Addition Stories

CA Standard
KEY NS 2.1

_____

— — — —

_____

_____

— — — —

_____

Directions: Tell an addition story. Show your story with bear counters. Draw the bears. Write how many in all.

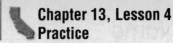
Use Pictures to Add

CA Standard
KEY NS 2.1

_____

‒ ‒ ‒ ‒ ‒ ‒ ‒ ‒ ‒

_____

_____

‒ ‒ ‒ ‒ ‒ ‒ ‒ ‒ ‒

_____

_____

‒ ‒ ‒ ‒ ‒ ‒ ‒ ‒ ‒

_____

_____

‒ ‒ ‒ ‒ ‒ ‒ ‒ ‒ ‒

Directions: Use counters to tell a story about the picture. Write how many in all.

Name _____

Problem Solving: Use a Picture

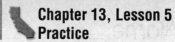

CA Standard
KEY NS 2.1

_____   _____   _____

– – – – –   and   – – – – – –   – – – – –   in all

_____   _____

_____   _____   _____

– – – – –   and   – – – – – –   – – – – –   in all

_____   _____

3

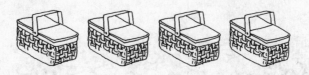

_____   _____   _____

– – – –   and   – – – –   – – – – –   in all

_____   _____

Directions: Tell a story to match the pictures. Use counters to model the story. Write the numbers and then write how many in all.

Name _____

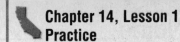
Hands On: Model Subtraction

CA Standard
KEY NS 2.1

 1

_____

- - - - - - -

_____

 2

_____

- - - - - - -

_____

 3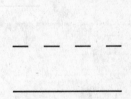

_____

- - - - - - -

_____

 4

_____

- - - - - - -

_____

Directions: 1–4 Count how many in all. Use counters to model a story. Write how many are left.

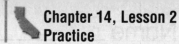
Hands On: Subtract with Cubes

CA Standard
KEY NS 2.1

⭐ **1** _____

🍃 **2** _____

🍎 **3** _____

- - - - - -   - - - - - -   - - - - - -

_____   _____   _____

Directions: **1** Place cubes on the kittens. Count. Write the number. **2** Take away cubes to show the kittens leaving the group. Write the number. **3** Write how many kittens are left.

Use with text pp. 193–194

Name _____

Hands On: Subtraction Stories

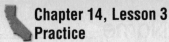

CA Standard
KEY NS 2.1

_____
_ _ _ _ _
_____

_____
_ _ _ _ _
_____

Directions: Tell a subtraction story. Show your story with counters. Draw the bears. Circle and cross out the ones you take away. Write how many are left.

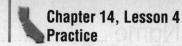
Use Pictures to Subtract

CA Standard
KEY NS 2.1

 1

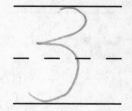

 2

 3

 4

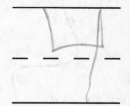

Directions: Use counters to tell a story about the pictures. Count how many in all. Circle and cross out the group of animals that is leaving. Write how many are left.

Name _____

Problem Solving:
Draw a Picture

CA Standard
NS 2.0

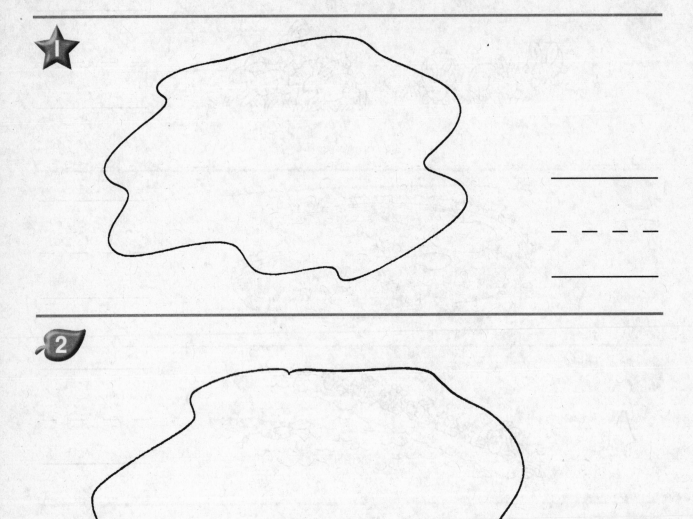

1 ⭐

_____

- - - - - - - - -

_____

2 🍃

_____

- - - - - - - - -

_____

Directions: 1–2 Listen to the story and draw a picture to tell the story. **1** Five ducks are in the grass. Two leave to go the pond. How many ducks are left?. Write the number. **2** Seven kites are flying in the sky. Three float down. How many are left? Write the number.

Use with text pp. 199–200

Hands On: Join Parts

CA Standard
NS 2.0

Whole	
Part	Part

1 7 + 2 = _____

2 2 + 3 = _____

3 8 + 1 = _____

Directions: Read the addition sentence. Place counters in each part to match the numbers. Move all the counters to the whole. Count. Write how many in all.

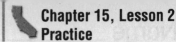

Hands On: Separate Parts

CA Standard
NS 2.0

Whole	
Part	**Part**

⭐ **1**

9 – 2 =

7

 2

5 – 1 =

4

3

7 – 2 =

5

Directions: Read the addition sentence. Place counters in the whole to show the first number. Move counters from the whole to one part show the second number. Write how many are left.

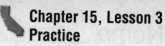
Hands On: Addition and Subtraction Patterns

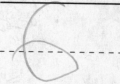
CA Standard
KEY NS 2.1

 1

$$5 \quad + \quad 1 \quad = \quad 6$$

 2

$$6 \quad + \quad 1 \quad = \quad 7$$

 3

$$5 \quad - \quad 1 \quad = \quad 4$$

 4

$$6 \quad - \quad 1 \quad = \quad 5$$

Directions: 1–2 Use counters to show each number. Count the counters. Write how many in all. 3–4 Show the first number with counters. Take away one counter. Write how many are left.

Use with text pp. 216A–216D

Hands On: Relate Addition and Subtraction

CA Standard
KEY NS 2.1

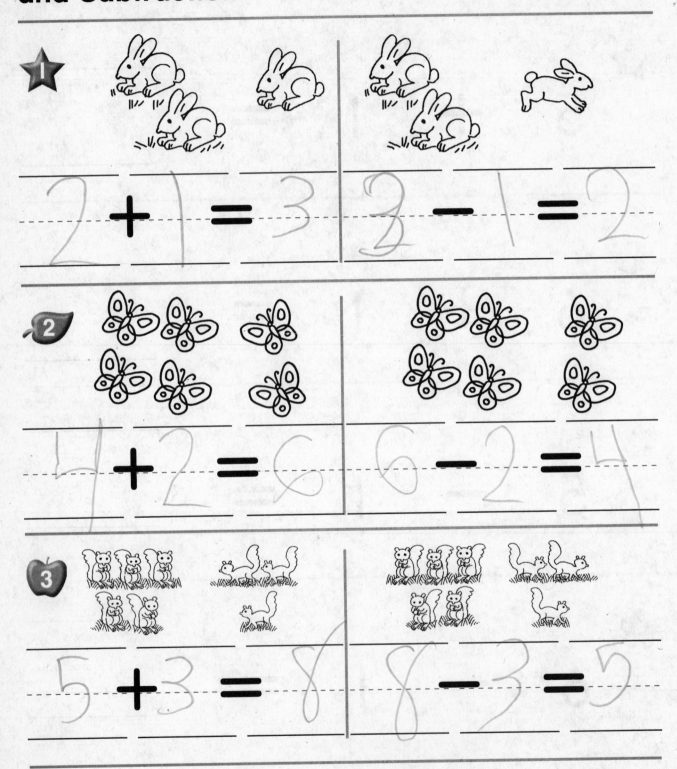

⭐ 1

$2 + 1 = 3$ $3 - 1 = 2$

🍃 2

$4 + 2 = 6$ $6 - 2 = 4$

🍎 3

$5 + 3 = 8$ $8 - 3 = 5$

Directions: 1–3 Write the addition sentence. Then circle and cross out the ones leaving. Write the subtraction sentence.

Use with text pp. 216E–216H

Name _____

Problem Solving: Act It Out

CA Standard
KEY NS 2.1

_____

- - - - - - - - - -

_____

_____

- - - - - - - - - -

_____

Directions: 1 – 2 Listen to the story. Use counters to act out the story. 1 Five dogs play in a park. Two more join them. How many are there in all? Write the number. 2 Six bees buzz around a flower. Two fly away. How many are left? Write the number.

73
Use with text pp. 217A–218

Name _____

Hands On: Record Addition

CA Standard
KEY NS 2.1

Directions: Tell a story about how the picture shows adding one. Write how many in all.

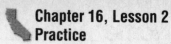
Hands On: Record Subtraction

CA Standard
KEY NS 2.1

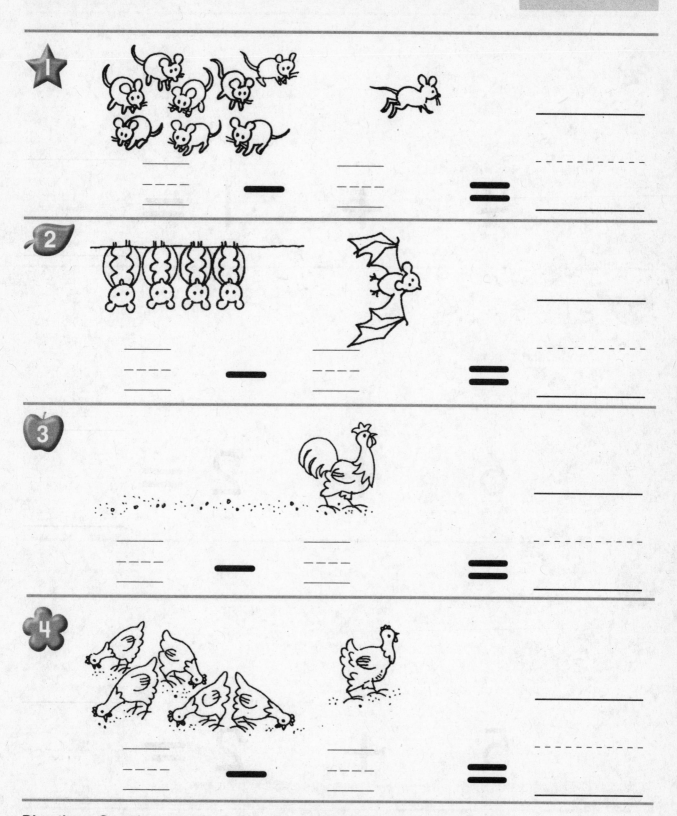

Directions: Count how many in all. Write the number. Circle and cross out the one that is leaving. Write the number. Count how many are left. Write the number.

Hands On: Add 1 or 2

CA Standard
KEY NS 2.1

$$4 \quad + \quad 1 \quad = \quad 5$$

$$6 \quad + \quad 2 \quad = \quad 8$$

$$5 \quad + \quad 2 \quad = \quad 7$$

Directions: Show each number with counters. Draw the counters. Write how many in all.

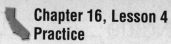

Hands On: Subtract 1 or 2

CA Standard
KEY NS 2.1

$$6 - 2 = $$

$$7 - 1 = $$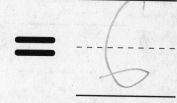

$$4 - 2 = $$

Directions: Show the first number with counters. Draw the counters. Circle and cross out 1 or 2. Write how many are left.

Name _____

Problem Solving: Use a Picture

  7   2

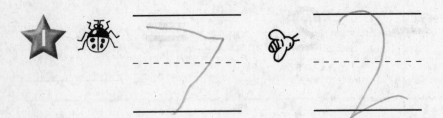

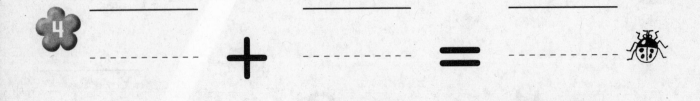

Directions: 1–2 Count how many ladybugs and bees are in each picture. Write the numbers. **3–4** Make a number sentence to show how many bees and ladybugs you see in all.

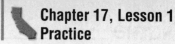

Hands On: Numbers 10–19

CA Standard
NS 1.2

12

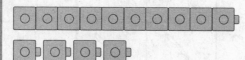

14

19

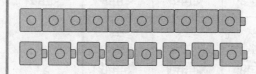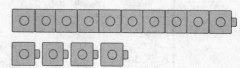

15

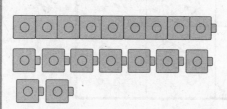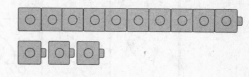

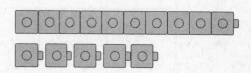

Directions: Count the cubes. Circle the set that matches the number.

Name _____

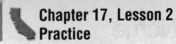
Hands On: Numbers 10–12

CA Standards
NS 1.2, MR 1.2

 1

 3

 2

 4

_____

- - - - - - - -

_____

Directions: Count the objects. Write the number.

Name _____

Hands On: Numbers 13–15

CA Standards
NS 1.2, MR 1.2

 1.

_____

- - - - - - - - - - -

 2.

_____

- - - - - - - - - - -

 3.
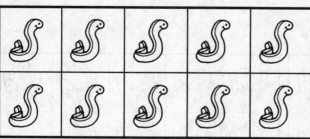

_____

- - - - - - - - - - -

 4.
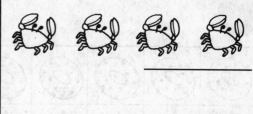

_____

- - - - - - - - - - -

Directions: Count the filled ten frame as 10. Count on. Write the number.

Use with text pp. 247–248

Name _____

Hands On: Numbers 16–19

CA Standards
NS 1.2, MR 1.2

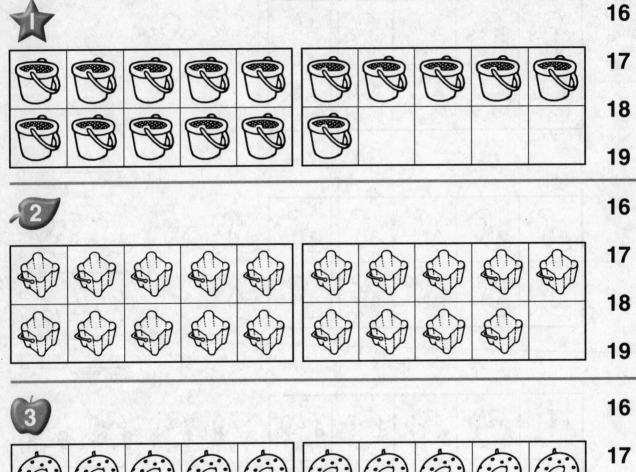

⭐ **1**	16 17 18 19
🍃 **2**	16 17 18 19
🍎 **3**	16 17 18 19
🌸 **4**	16 17 18 19

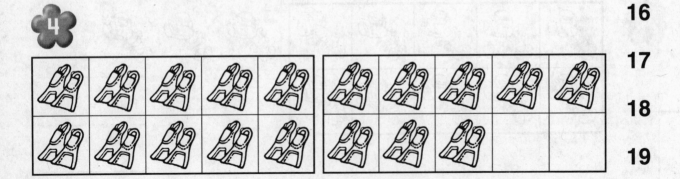

Directions: Count the items. Circle the number.

Use with text pp. 249–250

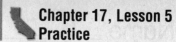
Problem Solving: Use a Graph

CA Standard
NS 1.2

Dan's Shells

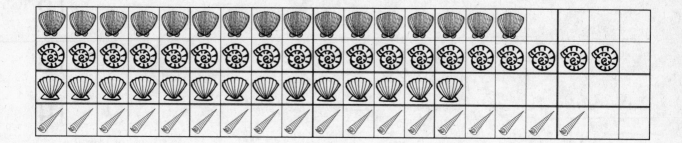

_____   _____   _____   _____

- - - - - - - - - -   - - - - - - - - - -   - - - - - - - - - -   - - - - - - - - - -

_____   _____   _____   _____

Directions: **1** Count how many shells of each kind are shown. Write the number. **2–3** Circle the kind of shell that Dan has more of.

Name _____

Hands On: Show Parts 11–14

CA Standard
KEY NS 1.0

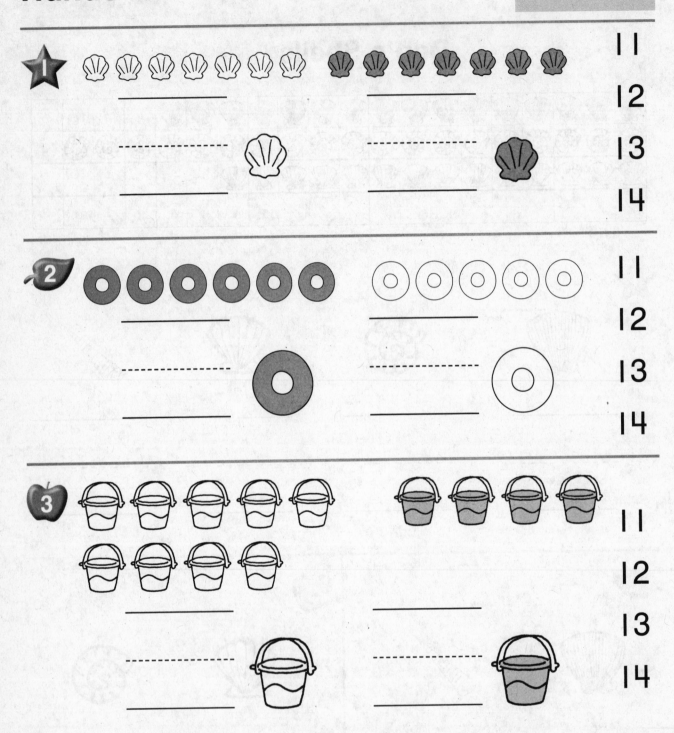

Directions: Count the number of items of each color. Write the numbers. Count how many in all. Circle the number.

Name _____

Hands On: Show Parts 15–19

1   15
16
17
18
19

2   15
16
17
18
19

3   15
16
17
18
19

4   15
16
17
18
19

Directions: Count the number of items of each color. Write the numbers. Count how many in all. Circle the number.

Order Numbers Through 19

CA Standard
NS 1.2

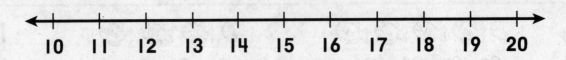

10 11 12 13 14 15 16 17 18 19 20

⭐ 1

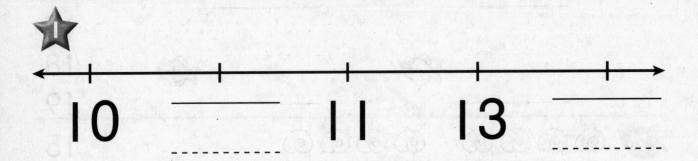

10 ____ 11 13 ____

🍃 2

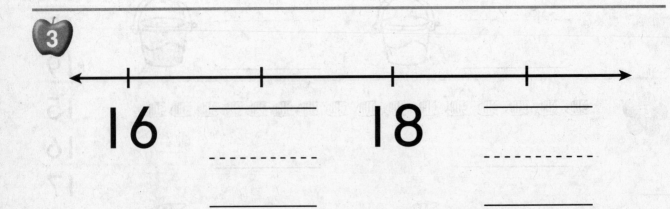

14 15 ____ 17

🍎 3

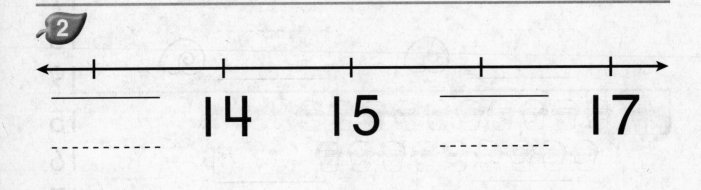

16 18

Directions: Write the missing numbers.

Estimate Quantities Through 19

CA Standard
NS 1.3

 1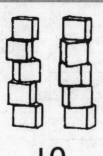

10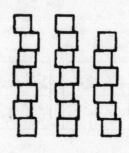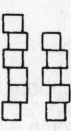

 2

15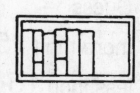

 3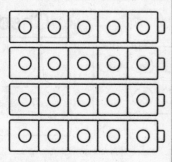

20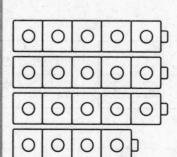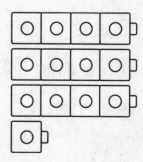

 4

15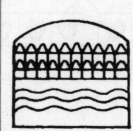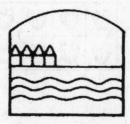

Directions: Circle the set that has about the same number as the first set.

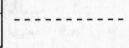
Problem Solving: Guess and Check

CA Standard
NS 3.1

1

Guess

more than 15

less than 15

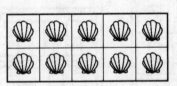

Check
_____
- - - - - - - - - -
_____

2

Guess

more than 15

less than 15

 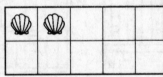

Check
_____
- - - - - - - - - -
_____

3

Guess

more than 15

less than 15

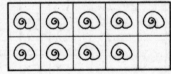

Check
_____
- - - - - - - - - -
_____

4

Guess

more than 15

less than 15

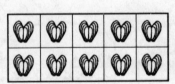

Check
_____
- - - - - - - - - -
_____

Directions: Guess whether the picture shows more than 15 or less than 15. Circle your guess. Count to check your answer. Write the number.

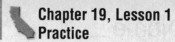

Hands On: Read a Calendar

CA Standard
MG 1.2

			June			
Sunday	Monday	Tuesday	Wednesday	Thursday	Friday	Saturday
					1	2
3	4	5	6	7	8	9
10	11	12	13	14	15	16
17	18	19	20	21	22	23
24	25	26	27	28	29	30

Sunday   Monday   Tuesday

Wednesday   Thursday   Friday

Directions: 1 Find June 11. Circle the date on the calendar. Circle the day of the week it falls on. **2** Find June 20. Circle the date on the calendar. Circle the day of the week it falls on.

Practice Book
89
Use with text pp. 277–278

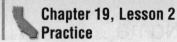
Times of Day

CA Standard
KEY MG 1.0

Directions: Circle the picture that shows: **1** the morning; **2** the afternoon; **3** the evening.

Name _____

Days of the Week

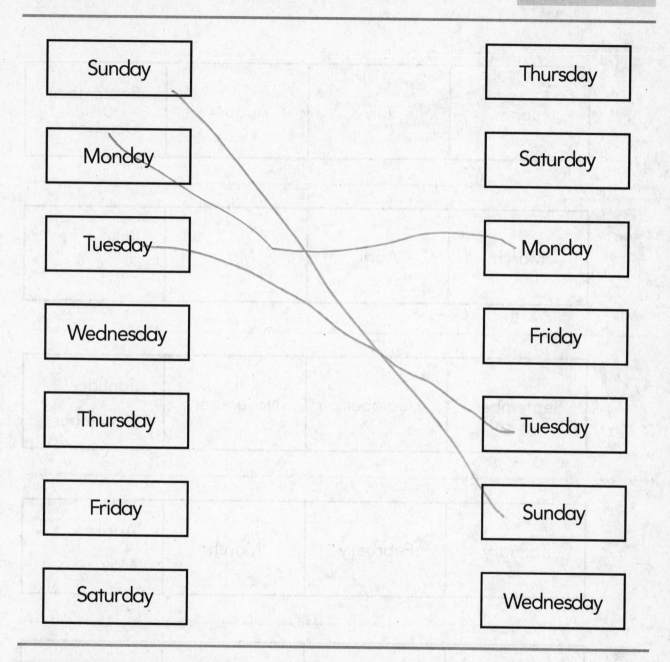

Sunday		Thursday
Monday		Saturday
Tuesday		Monday
Wednesday		Friday
Thursday		Tuesday
Friday		Sunday
Saturday		Wednesday

Directions: Say the names of the days of the week. Draw a line to match each day to the list on the right.

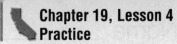
Months of the Year

CA Standard
MG 1.2

 1

June	July	August	September October

2

March	April	May	July June

3

September	October	November	January December

4

January	February	March	April May

5

May	June	July	September August

Directions: 1–5 Circle the correct fourth month.

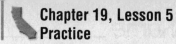
Problem Solving: Use a Picture

CA Standard
MG 1.3

May

Sunday	Monday	Tuesday	Wednesday	Thursday	Friday	Saturday
				1	2	3
4	5	6	7	8	9	10
11	12	13	14	15	16	17
18	19	20	21	22	23	24
25	26	27	28	29	30	31

⭐1 _____

Saturdays

2 _____

Thursdays

🍎3 _____

Fridays

🌸4 _____

Wednesdays

Directions: Count and write the number of: **1** Saturdays; **2** Thursdays;
3 Fridays; **4** Wednesdays. Circle the first Tuesday in blue, the last Monday in red,
and all the Sundays in green.

Use with text pp. 285–286

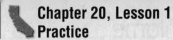
Hands On: Hours and Minutes

CA Standard
KEY MG 1.0

Directions: Circle the activity if it takes about a minute to do. Underline the activity if it takes about an hour to do.

Use with text pp. 290B–290C

Name _____

Hands On: Estimate with Time

CA Standard
KEY MG 1.0

1 ★

1   10

2 🍃

4   14

3 🍎

3   30

4 🌸

5   45

5 🌲

2   20

6 🦋

6   60

Directions: Circle the number of times in a minute you think you can do each task.

Name _____

Time to the Hour

_____

- - - - - - - - -

_____ o'clock

_____

- - - - - - - - -

_____ o'clock

 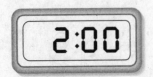

_____

- - - - - - - - -

_____ o'clock

_____

- - - - - - - - -

_____ o'clock

_____

- - - - - - - - -

_____ o'clock

Directions: Write the time shown on the clock.

Practice Book

96

Use with text pp. 291–292

Name _____

Relate Time to Events

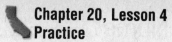

CA Standard
MG 1.4

Directions: Draw a line from the event to the time it might happen.

Use with text pp. 293–294

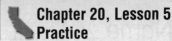

Problem Solving: Act It Out

CA Standard
MG 1.4

   1 hour

   3 hours

   4 hours

  2 hours

Directions: 1–4 Look at the event and read the clock. See how many hours pass. Add the hour hand to each clock to show when each event ends.

98

Hands On: Twenty

CA Standard
NS 1.2

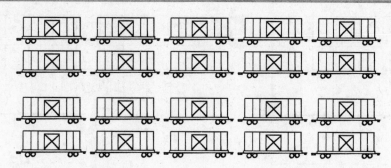

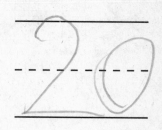

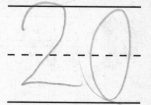

Directions: Count the train cars and circle groups of 10. Write the number that tells how many in all.

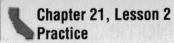

Numbers 21–25

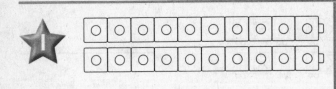

Directions: Count the cube trains by tens and then count on. Write the number.

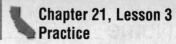
Numbers 26–30

CA Standard
NS 1.2

 1

25   26   27

 2

28   29   30

 3

27   28   29

4

25   26   27

5

27   28   29

6

27   28   29

Directions: Count the cube trains by tens and then count on. Circle the number.

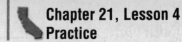
Hands On: Order Numbers 0–30

CA Standard
NS 1.2

 1. ___ ___ ___

2 ___ **4** ___ **6** ___

 2. ___ ___

___ **10 11** ___ **13**

 3. ___ ___

15 ___ **17 18** ___

4. ___ ___

___ **21 22** ___ **24**

 5. ___ ___

26 ___ **28 29** ___

Directions: Write the missing numbers.

Problem Solving: Reasonable Answers

CA Standards
NS 3.0, NS 3.1

1

less than 25
more than 25

_____

- - - - - - - - - -

_____

2

less than 25
more than 25

_____

- - - - - - - - - -

_____

3

less than 25
more than 25

_____

- - - - - - - - - -

_____

4

less than 25
more than 25

_____

- - - - - - - - - -

_____

Directions: Estimate whether there are less than or more than 25 items in each collection. Circle the estimate. Count the number of items there are in all. Write the number.

Name _____

Hands On: Estimate

CA Standards
NS 3.0, NS 3.1

1

2

3

4

Directions: Circle the set that you estimate has about the same number as the first set.

Name _____

Estimation

CA Standards
NS 3.0, NS 3.1

 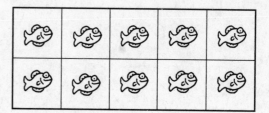

10
20
30

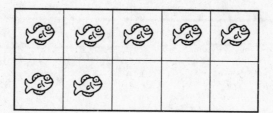

 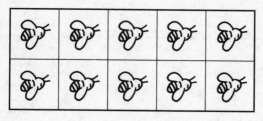

10
20
30

10
20
30

Directions: Circle an estimate for the total number of items.

Use with text pp. 321–322

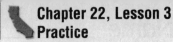

Compare Quantities

CA Standard
NS 1.3

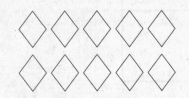

Directions: **1–2** Circle the set of items that has less. **3–4** Circle the set of items that has more.

Calendar: Use Numbers 1–31

CA Standard
KEY MG 1.0

Sunday	Monday	Tuesday	Wednesday	Thursday	Friday	Saturday

Directions: Make a calendar for your birthday month. Write the name of the month and dates.

Problem Solving: Use Logical Thinking

CA Standards
NS 1.3

| 28 | 17 | |

| | 16 | 21 |

| 30 | | 13 |

Directions: 1–3 Write the missing number. 1 Circle the set that has more than 20 but less than 25.
2 Circle the set that has more than 10 but less than 15. 3 Circle the set that has more than 25 but less than 30.

Hands On: Solids

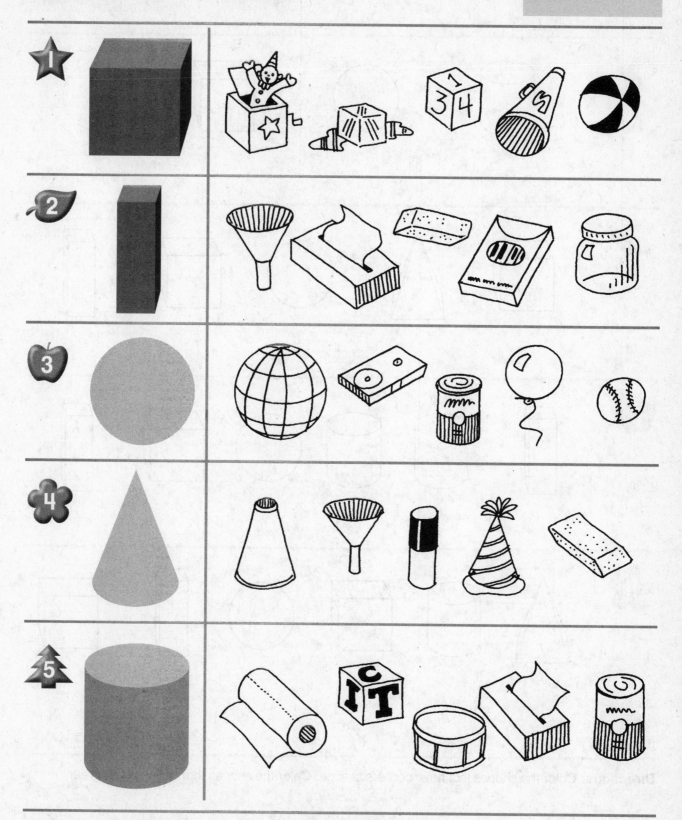

Directions: Circle the objects that are like the solid shape.

Name _____

Hands On: Sort Solids

CA Standard
MG 2.2

    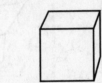

Directions: Color the shapes that have corners orange. Color the shapes that have curves green.

Hands On: Combine and Separate Plane Shapes

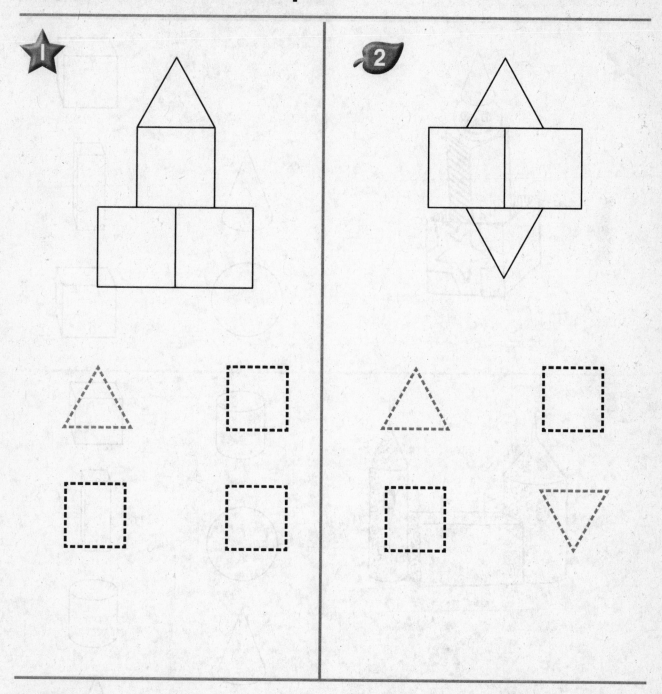

Directions: Cut out the shapes. Combine them to make each figure. Paste them to show the shape.

Name _____

Combine and Separate Solid Shapes

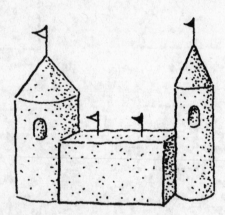

Directions: 1 Color the shapes that were used to make the Jack-in-the-box. **2** Color the kind of shapes that were used to make the sandcastle.

Use with text pp. 347–348

Problem Solving: Use Logical Reasoning

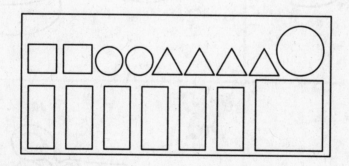

Directions: Color in a shape and then cross it out in the box.

Hands On: Compare Length

CA Standard
KEY MG 1.0

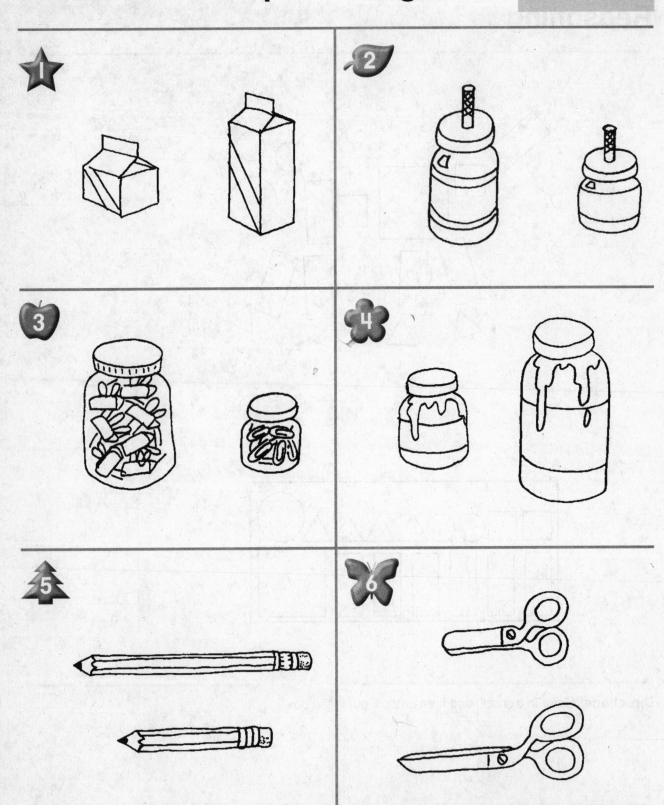

Directions: 1–4 Circle the taller one. Underline the shorter one. 5–6 Circle the
longer one. Underline the shorter one.

Name _____

Sort by Length

CA Standard
KEY MG 1.0

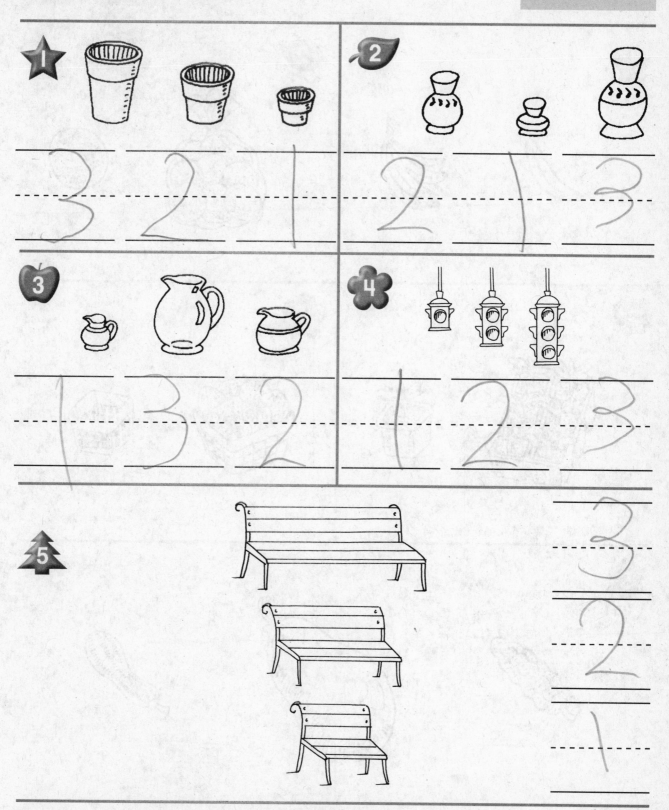

Directions: 1–4 Write the numbers *1, 2,* and *3* to order the items from shortest to tallest.
5 Write the numbers *1, 2,* and *3* to order the items from shortest to longest.

115

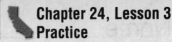

Hands On: Compare Weights

CA Standard
KEY MG 1.0

Directions: **1–4** Circle the heavier one. Underline the lighter one. **5** Circle the two that are about the same weight.

Name _____

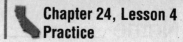
Hands On: Compare Capacity

CA Standard
KEY MG 1.0

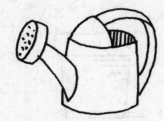

Directions: 1–2 Draw something that holds more. 3 Draw something that holds less. 4 Draw
something that holds about the same.

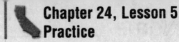
Problem Solving:
Use Logical Reasoning

CA Standard
KEY MG 1.0

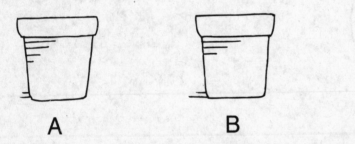

A   B   C

2

Directions: **1** Draw 3 flowers. Make Flower C taller than Flower A. Make Flower A taller than Flower B.
2 Draw three baskets. Draw a red basket that holds more than a yellow basket. Draw a blue basket that
holds less than a yellow basket.

Practice Book

118

Use with text pp. 359–360